PassAlong
Arch® Books

Baby
Prince of Peace

Carol Greene
Illustrated by Michelle Dorenkamp

Make a New Friend in Jesus

PassAlong Arch® Books help you share Jesus with friends close to you and with children all around the world!

When you've enjoyed this story, pass it along to a friend.   When your friend is finished, mail this book to the address below. Concordia Gospel Outreach promises to deliver your book to a boy or girl somewhere in the world to help him or her learn about Jesus.

Myself

My name _____

My address _____

_____

My PassAlong Friend

My name _____

My address _____

_____

When you're ready to give your PassAlong Arch® Book to a new friend who doesn't know about Jesus, mail it to

**Concordia Gospel Outreach
3547 Indiana Avenue
St. Louis, MO 63118**

PassAlong Series

God's Good Creation
Noah's Floating Zoo
Baby Moses' River Ride
Jonah's Fishy Adventure
Baby Jesus, Prince of Peace
Jesus Stills the Storm
Jesus' Big Picnic
God's Easter Plan

Baby Jesus Prince of Peace

Luke 2:1–16 for Children

Carol Greene
Illustrated by Michelle Dorenkamp

he prophet spoke in days of old.
His voice was strong. His words were bold.
"Behold! A maiden shall give birth.
Her Child, God's Son, shall rule the earth.

"And we shall call Him Prince of peace,
For where He rules, all wars shall cease,
And sin and death shall hold no fear.
Behold! The time is coming near."

"Let's turn the page and find out."

"Time for what?"

Along a dusty, winding road,
A little donkey bears his load.
Young Mary, great with Child, must ride,
While patient Joseph plods beside.

To Bethlehem they make their way.
"We'll count you there," the rulers say.
The sky grows dark. The day is gone.
And still they travel, on and on.

"Why do Mary and Joseph have to be counted?"

"So the emperor can see how many people he rules."

The road is cold. The road is long.
It seems no place for donkey song.
But sing out, little donkey. Bray!
The Prince of peace is on His way.

"Who is the Prince of peace?"

"I'm not sure—yet!"

At Bethlehem the inns are filled.
Young Mary shivers, tired and chilled.
But then a landlord, by God's grace,
Says, "You may use my stable-place."

And there as midnight moves to morn,
The tiny Prince of peace is born.
The quiet oxen see His birth,
This Child God sent to rule the earth.

Sing, you oxen, large and slow.
    Songs of welcome rumble low.
    As He rests on Mary's arm,
    Your straw-sweet breath will keep Him
        warm.

"He's so tiny."

"The tiny Prince of peace."

Young Mary smiles down at her Son,
A helpless Babe, and yet the One
The prophet long ago foretold
In voice so strong, in words so bold.

She thinks of when the angel came
And told her of the Baby's name.
Still smiling, she stands up to lay
Her Jesus on the manger hay.

"Shouldn't a prince have a royal bed?"

"I think He likes the manger."

Sing, young Mary! Sing with joy
As you gaze at your newborn Boy.
In God's great plan you've played your
    part.
Now sing a glad song in your heart.

"Mary seems so happy."

"Yes!"

The fields are dark. The fields are still.
And sleepy shepherds drowse until
God's glory shatters through the night.
Then sleepy shepherds shake with fright.

An angel speaks, "Oh, do not fear.
I bring you joy. I bring you cheer.
At Bethlehem near break of morn,
The Savior of the world was born!"

Stop your shaking, shepherds. Sing!
This news changes everything.
The Lamb of God has come to save.
So stand up, shepherds. Sing! Be brave!

"I'm not scared. Are you?"

"Not a bit!"

The angel says, "Now God designed
A sign for you. The Babe you'll find
In swaddling clothes on bed of hay.
He's lying there this very day."

Then round the angel rank on rank
Of angels gather, all to thank
And praise the Lord with holy mirth,
Because He sent His Son to earth.

Sing, you angels. Glory sing.
Let all earth and heaven ring.
Let your songs our songs increase.
Glory, glory, good will, peace!

"Glory!"

And when the angel song is through,
The shepherds know what they must do.
At once to Bethlehem they run
To find the Prince of peace, God's Son.

Into the stable dark and small
They crowd, those shepherds, sheep
and all.
And Baby hand holds woolly fleece,
The tiny, sleepy Prince of peace.

"Poor Baby."

"So sleepy."

Sing a lullaby. Oh, sing!
Let the little sheepbells ring.
Gently now, you woolly sheep,
Sing the Prince of peace to sleep.

That little Prince, so humbly born,
Would someday die with cross and thorn,
But, raised by God to life above,
Now rules the earth with peace and love.

No earthly throne sets Him apart.
Instead, He rules within each heart,
And when we all our struggling cease,
We feel His love. We know His peace.

"There never was a Baby like this before."

"Never ever."

Sing, you heavens! Sing, you earth!
Sing about the Christmas birth.
Sin and death and war shall cease.
He's come, the tiny Prince of peace.